Madame Curie
Albert Einstein

PENDULUM ILLUSTRATED SERIES

Pendulum Press, Inc.
West Haven, Connecticut

ISBN 0-88301-424-6 Complete Set
0-88301-356-8 Paperback
0-88301-368-1 Hardcover

Library of Congress Catalog Card Number 79-83641

Published by
Pendulum Press, Inc.
An Academic Industries, Inc. Company
The Academic Building
Saw Mill Road
West Haven, Connecticut 06516

Printed in the United States of America

To the teacher

Every parent and teacher knows that youngsters often model their lives after those of people they admire. Sometimes this works well, as in the case of a boy named Erich Weiss. Reading the biography of the French magician Houdin, Erich was so fascinated that he changed his name and eventually became the great Houdini, the world-famous escape artist. But children don't always choose worthwhile models; we shudder to think they might imitate one or another of the unsavory characters they see on TV. It is precisely to counterbalance this mix of dubious screen heroes that Pendulum presents its illustrated biography series.

Like the Pendulum illustrated classics series that preceded them, these biographies are the result of painstaking research and writing. The artwork throughout is first-quality illustration; the type, an easy-to-read sans-serif style. Tested with both the Dale-Chall List and the Fry Readability Scale, each book is edited to an intermediate-grade vocabulary level. Yet the material is suitable for practically everyone regardless of age or reading prowess.

How you, the teacher, will use this series is of great interest to us. We have tried to provide you with a varied, interesting, and self-motivating teaching tool. We think your students will like our selection of famous people and the format we used to illustrate their lives. If you or they have any questions, suggestions, or comments on the series, we would like to hear them. As always, Pendulum wants to provide your students with the best materials possible.

The editors

Madame Curie

Written by
NAUNERLE C. FARR

Illustrated by
NESTOR LEONIDEZ

a
VINCENT FAGO
production

Contents

Childhood in Poland 5-10

The young teacher 11-15

Learning and experimenting at the Sorbonne 16-21

Studying radioactivity 22-29

Questions for review 30-33

On a May night in 1902, in Paris, France, Marie and Pierre Curie went to the old shed where Marie had been working. In the dark they saw a beautiful blue light. It was the glow of radium.*
Marie Curie was the first great woman scientist.** Thanks to her work, doctors would one day be able to use radium to treat people with cancer.***

*a metal that gives off heat rays

**someone who studies the laws of nature

***a disease that causes abnormal cells to grow in the body

Marie was born Marya Sklodovska in Warsaw, Poland, in 1867.
My dear children—you have a new sister, Marya!
When can we see her?

Marya's father was a teacher. Even as a small child, Marya loved to watch him work.
You like to help me, don't you?
Yes!
Marya never forgot the things her father showed her. She wanted to grow up to be just like him.

At this time, Warsaw was in a part of Poland ruled by Russia. People were not allowed to study the history of Poland. They even had to speak Russian instead of their own language.*
But some brave teachers secretly taught their students about Poland's history.
Marya, tell us about Stanislas Augustus.
He was king of Poland in 1764.
*Everyone knew that what they were doing was a crime.** So they kept their lessons quiet.*

*the language spoken in Russia

**something that is against the law

One day during their history lesson, a bell rang.
Quick, girls! Hide your books!
Four girls began gathering up the books and papers.
They took them to another room.
Get out your sewing!
The girls returned to their seats just as the door opened. The headmistress* came in with the Russian inspector** of schools.
This is a sewing class. While the girls work, I read them Russian stories.
I see.

*the woman who is in charge of a school for girls

**a person who checks things to see if they are running correctly

The inspector opened all the desks. But he found nothing.
I want to question one of your pupils.
Very well. Marya Sklodovska, please stand.
Marya had hoped she wouldn't be called on. But she was always chosen because she was the best student in the class.
She stood to answer the inspector's questions.
Name the czars* who have ruled since Catherine II.
Paul I, Alexander I, Nicholas I. . . .
Later Marya won a scholarship** to the high school. She talked to her sister, Bronya, about it.
Should I go? It's a Russian school, and they are our enemies!
Of course you must go!
The Russians don't want us to learn. Anyone as smart as you must learn all you can!

*Russian kings

**an award of money given to help pay for one's schooling

So Marya went to the high school. In June, 1883, she graduated.*
The gold medal for the best student goes to Marya Sklodovska!

Her father was proud of her.

I would like you to spend next year visiting our relatives** in the country.
But, Papa . . . I expected to go to work!

You are only fifteen years old. You have spent most of your life studying hard! Now you must have fun!

So Marya went to the country. Her aunts gave her good food. Her uncles taught her to ride horses. And her cousins took her to parties.

Look! My shoes are worn out from dancing!
Wait until the next party. You will dance for two days and nights!

*finished school and received a diploma

**aunts, uncles, cousins

Soon the night of the big party came. The girls climbed into sleighs. * *Their escorts* * * *rode beside them.*

Where are we going?
You'll see! It's a magic journey!

They rode from village to village. Along the way, other sleighs joined them. Some people rode in front of the sleighs, playing music.

Sometimes they stopped at big houses where they ate and danced.
It's wonderful! How long does it go on?
For another day and night!

*open coaches on runners that are pulled by horses over snow and ice

**dates for dances or parties

But the party ended at last. And so did Marya's wonderful year. In September, she returned to Warsaw.
I want to earn money so I can help Papa. And I want to help you become a doctor, too.
Thank you! But how will you do it?
I am writing notes to people asking for a job as a teacher.
But not many people wanted lessons. And those who did made teaching hard work for Marya.
My son needs a teacher. But you are much too young!
Sonny *needs* reading lessons, but he doesn't want them.
I *won't* learn to read!
I don't have the money to pay you now.
Marya seemed to spend all her time walking from job to job. She made very little money.

I have found a job in the country with a family that needs a teacher for their children.
Live in the country? Leave Papa? Why should you do that for me?
Bronya, you've been waiting for years to become a doctor. You can help me later.
So Bronya went to Paris to enter the Sorbonne.* And in January, 1886, eighteen-year-old Marya went to the country home of the Zs.
Miss Sklodovska.
Come in, my dear! Take off your coat! Warm yourself with hot tea!
Later, Marya met the children she was to teach.
This is Bronka, my oldest daughter. This is Andzia, and this is Julek. They will be your pupils.
I am glad you have come!

*a well-known university

The family was friendly, and Marya got along well. Then one day the oldest son, Casimir, came home for the holidays.
I've never known a girl like you! You do everything so well!
Marya, I love you! Will you marry me?
Yes, Casimir.
But Casimir's parents were not pleased.
You want to marry a governess?* Never!
Oh, Casimir, you must be crazy!
So Casimir returned to school, and Marya went on with her teaching. No more was said about the marriage.
Bronya needs the money I send, so I must stay here! I will forget about love.

*a woman who is hired by a family to teach and take care of the children

For three years Marya worked with her pupils. In her spare time, she studied whatever books she could find. When she had almost given up hope, things began to change for the better.
Papa writes that everyone is doing well. He says I should save my money for myself!
Spring came, and there was more good news.
Bronya is going to marry a young doctor. They want me to live with them and study at the Sorbonne!
But it is too late for me. Too many years have passed.
Instead of going to Paris, Marya returned to Warsaw and took a new job. She saw her father often. And one evening she visited a cousin.
This looks like such an important place!
We fooled the Russians into thinking it is a museum.* But back here we have a laboratory** where we can work in secret.

*a building where objects are exhibited for the public

**a place where scientists work and make experiments

Here we teach science* to our own people. You can study here, too, Marya.

From that day on, Marya knew what she wanted to do. She spent every free moment in the laboratory. And she saved all the money she could. At last, she wrote Bronya that she could come to Paris.

I have enough money.
Please take it, my dear.

Finally the day came to leave.
I sent my trunk ahead. I have a blanket and food for the train ride.

Soon I'll come back to you and stay!
Yes, my dear! Good luck!

*the study of the laws of nature

Three days later, Marya reached Paris. She went to the apartment where Bronya lived with her new husband, Casimir Dluski.
You are here at last!
Welcome, little sister!
I will show you your room. It's small, but quiet.
Please . . . could I see the Sorbonne first?
Following Bronya's directions, she took a bus to the Sorbonne.
France—where the people are free!
At last she reached the Sorbonne.
FRENCH REPUBLIC
FACULTY OF SCIEN
FIRST QUARTER
CLASSES WILL BEGIN AT THE SORBONNE ON NOV. 3 1891
What great things I will learn here!

She went in, paid her money, and signed up for classes.
Your name?
Marya . . . no, *Marie* Sklodovska! From now on I will use the French spelling!
Soon classes began.
I thought I knew so much. But I know nothing! I must study, study, study!
But it was often hard for Marie to study. The Dluskis liked to give parties, and there was always music.
Sometimes a young pianist,* Ignace Paderewski, would play for them. Marie could not study as hard as she wished to.
And so . . .
I'm going to look for a room closer to my school.
You will not have enough money to live on!

*someone who plays the piano as his life's work

But Marie moved anyway. She found an attic* room. It had only a lamp for light, a small stove for heat, and a pitcher with which to bring water from downstairs.
No one bothered her. She could study most of the night if she wanted to.

Sometimes she even forgot to eat. She grew pale and thin. One day she fainted on the stairs, and a friend ran for Casimir Dluski.
What's wrong?
The little one has been starving herself! Put her to bed and feed her!

But no one could stop Marie from studying. And after final examinations,** the best student was named.
First in the class is Marie Sklodovska!

*the small part of a building just beneath the roof

**tests given at the end of a course of study

Marie spent that summer in Warsaw. When she returned to Paris, she was well rested.

Soon she spoke to friends about a problem.
I have a chance to do some research* on my own, but there is no laboratory large enough.
A friend of mine might have a place you could use.

Perhaps you have heard of him. His name is Pierre Curie.
Oh yes! He is a great scientist. He won't be interested in my work.

But Marie returned the next day to meet Pierre Curie.
Pierre, I want you to meet Marie Sklodovska.

It wasn't long before Pierre fell in love with Marie. Before she returned to Poland again, he asked her to marry him.

Oh, Pierre, I always put my work first. I never planned to marry!
And I did the same! But I never thought I would meet a girl who shared my interests.

*studying or experimenting done to learn new facts about something

I can't marry you. I must go home and do what I can for my country.
In Poland you can't go on with your studies. You must not give up your work!
But Marie left Pierre and Paris and went back to Warsaw.
When she returned to Paris in the fall, Pierre would not give up. At last, Marie said that she loved him.
We can be married at my parents' home. They love you very much!
And I love them. They remind me of my own family.
Pierre and Marie were married on July 26, 1895. Then they rode away on new bicycles for a trip through the country.
She will be happy with my Pierre. There's no one on earth like him!
And Marie will be a loving daughter!
When they returned to Paris, Marie bought a cookbook* and asked Bronya for help. She wanted to prepare good meals for Pierre.
Why do your meals turn out so well, and mine are terrible?
You will learn! You've never had to cook before!

*a book that contains recipes for fixing many foods

In September, 1897, a daughter was born to Marie and Pierre.
Isn't she the most beautiful baby you've ever seen?
We'll name her Irene.
But Marie still went to the laboratory for eight hours every day. She left the baby with a nurse.*
Do you promise to take her out for fresh air and sunshine?
Yes, indeed!
She and Pierre spent their evenings studying.
We know about the strange rays given off by uranium.** I want to find out what causes those rays.
You may find out something important!
I'll need my own place to work.
I'll speak to the man in charge of the school. There must be a room there you can use.

*a woman who takes care of a small baby

**a metal that gives off radio waves

Marie was offered a glassed-in porch. It had no heat, but she took it anyway and started her work.
I wonder if these rays can be found in any other metals.
To find out, Marie made more tests.
Pierre! I found today that thorium* gives off these rays, too.
That's wonderful!
What should we call these strange rays? How about "radioactivity?"**
Then Marie did tests to learn the amount of radioactivity in different metals. She was surprised by what she found.
I have done my tests over and over. There is more radioactivity here than there should be.

*a metal that is not too well known

**rays given off by certain metals

She spoke of her findings with Pierre.
Unless I have made a mistake, there must be an *unknown* element* present.

I know! You've made no mistake. You've discovered a *new* element. What will you call it?
I don't know.

Pierre stopped his own work so he could help Marie. Soon their tests showed that there must be two unknown elements.
The second element is more radiant** than the first. Perhaps we should name it *radium.*
If you find it, you may call it anything you wish!

The Curies knew many things about what these new elements could do. But for others to believe their findings, they had to see the elements and weigh them.

If what you say is true, you will have changed everything we believe.
Then we must prove it to you by finding pure radium!

*one of the basic substances that make up all living and non-living things

**bright, shining

*Marie had found the signs of the new elements in pitchblende.**
She would need tons of pitchblende to prove her findings.

How can we pay for it? And where can we work on so much of it?
At the mines they remove the uranium salts** to make glasses. They throw away the rest. Perhaps we could buy that left-over pitch-blende.

We can use this old shed for our work.
The roof leaks, and there is no heat or floor. But we will use it!

A friend arranged for the Curies to receive the pitchblende.
At last it arrived!

Now we can go to work!
You are like a child with a birthday gift!

Marie began working at once.

I will find the new elements if it takes a mountain of pitchblende!

*a brown-black substance that contains radium
**an element found in pitchblende

*For four years they carried on their research. Pierre also worked at his teaching job. Marie became a teacher, too, in order to help pay for their experiments.**

Pierre's father had come to live with them. One evening in 1902, Marie had some news for him.

Father, Marie has something to tell you!
We have done it! We have found the radium!

That night after Irene was asleep, they walked back to the old shed. In the dark they saw a beautiful light. No one had ever seen it before. It was the glow of radium.

Don't light the lamp. Just look! It is beautiful!

Soon everyone wanted radium. But what Marie had made from all her work was only enough to fill the tip of a teaspoon.

An American company wants to know how to make radium salts. Maybe they'll pay us to tell them.
That would be wrong! We should *share* what we know.

Pierre agreed. The Curies never tried to make money from what they had learned.

*tests carried out by scientists in a laboratory

In June, 1903, Marie won her Doctor of Science degree.*
Congratulations!
The Curies received many honors.
You are the first woman to be invited here!
I am glad I could come.
In December, the Curies shared the Nobel Prize** with Henri Becquerel, the man whose work had started them thinking about radioactivity.
Oh, Pierre. Now you can spend all your time doing research.
And we can even hire some-one to help us!
In 1904, Pierre was given a job at the Sorbonne. The Curies also had a new daughter.
Isn't she pretty?
Yes, like a little doll.

*a title one receives after many years of study in a certain field

**a yearly prize given to people whose work is very important

In 1906, the Curies rented a country cottage for the Easter holidays. It was a happy time for them.
Life with you has been wonderful, Marie.
The day after they returned from their holiday, Marie came back late from a shopping trip. She found two old friends waiting for her. Their faces frightened her.
Marie, there has been an accident. Pierre has been killed.
Oh, no!
Marie walked past her friends into the garden.
Once I said to Pierre that we could not live without each other.

But he said, "You are wrong! One must work just the same!" I will try.

Not long afterward, Marie was offered the job Pierre had held at the Sorbonne.

You are the first woman ever to be offered such a job in France!
I will try to do it well—for our children.

On November 5, the Hall of Science was crowded. Marie Curie was to give her first lecture. She entered, made a little bow, and began to speak.*

Let us think about what has happened in the field of physics** during the last ten years.
She used Pierre's notes and began where he had stopped just before his death.

Marie won many more prizes, one of them a second Nobel Prize in 1911. She was busy with a new laboratory being built in Paris.

It is on the street named after Pierre. It is the wonderful new laboratory Pierre always dreamed of!
RUE PIERRE CURIE
INSTITUT DE RADIUM
PAVILLON CURIE
Marie herself ran the laboratory for many years.

*a public speech given to teach people about a subject

**a branch of science that deals with such things as energy, electricity, and radioactivity

In 1921, she and her daughters visited the United States. At the White House, President Harding presented her with some radium paid for by a group of American women.

Irene soon married Frederic Joliot, a young scientist, and together they carried on the work of the Curies. In 1935, they, too, would share a Nobel Prize.
They gave a good lecture, didn't they?

Marie Curie died in 1934, poisoned by the radium she had worked with for so long.

Her last book came out a year after her death.
RADIOACTIVITY
MME. PIERRE CURIE
Professor
at the
SORBONNE
NOBEL PRIZE
IN
PHYSICS
NOBEL PRIZE
IN
CHEMISTRY
RADIOACTIVITY
CURIE
THE END

Do you remember?

In order to earn money for her sister's education, Marie worked as a:

a. sales clerk. b. governess. c. housemaid.

After her first visit to a laboratory, Marie knew that she wanted to:

a. become a scientist. b. study law. c. work with pottery.

Marie married Pierre Curie, who was a fellow:

a. athlete. b. lawyer. c. scientist.

Marie Curie discovered:

a. silver. b. radium. c. gold.

Words to know

Can you use these words in sentences of your own?

element	Nobel Prize	uranium
research	physics	museum
pitchblende	radium	czars

True or false

1. As a young woman, Marie Curie earned money in a teaching job.

2. After Pierre's death, Marie took the same teaching job he had held at the Sorbonne.

3. Marie died of food poisoning in 1934.

4. Today radium is often used to help cure arthritis.

5. Although Marie Curie was a great scientist, she had a hard time learning to cook.

Questions to think about and discuss

1. For what great discovery is Marie Curie known? What things set her apart from other women of her time?

2. What problems did Marie have to face in her studies and later in her experiments? How did she solve them?

3. What qualities did Marie have which helped her become such a great scientist? Of these, which qualities do you think are needed for success in *any* kind of work?

4. Do you think it is possible for a woman today to be both a good mother and a good job-holder? Why or why not? How did Marie Curie rate as a mother? Can you back up your opinion with facts from the book?

5. The Curies accepted no money for their discoveries. If *you* discovered an important new element, would you charge individuals or companies for your formulas? Why or why not?

Albert Einstein

Written by
NAUNERLE C. FARR

Illustrated by
NESTOR REDONDO

a
VINCENT FAGO
production

Contents

The student of mathematics 35-43

The professor 44-48

Einstein becomes famous 49-53

Working in the United States 54-59

Questions for review 60-63

ALBERT EINSTEIN

*Albert Einstein was born in Germany in 1879. He became one of the most well-known men of his time. In 1933, Einstein left Germany and came to the United States. Because World War II was coming, Germany was not a safe place for him to live. In 1940, he became a citizen of the United States. Einstein is best known for his theory of relativity.**

E = mc²
E stands for energy
m stands for matter
c² stands for the speed of light multiplied by itself.

One day when five-year-old Albert was ill, his father brought him a gift.
I have brought you a compass.
Thank you. What is it for?
Sailors use it to find their way on the ocean.

*a belief involving objects moving at certain speeds

No matter how I turn it, the needle always points north!
Space* looks empty, but there must be something there that moves this needle—something I can't see!
Albert thought often about his compass.
He had a happy family life. His mother often played music with her friends. Albert liked to listen.

*the sky, the heavens

Mrs. Einstein played the piano very well. But Albert enjoyed hearing the violin* even more.
One day. . .
This is for you! You will have violin lessons.
So Albert went to a music teacher.
Practice,** practice, practice!
Soon he played the violin well.
That is a pretty tune.
Thank you, Mama.
Playing the violin was a pleasure to Albert all his life.

*a small wooden instrument that is played by moving a bow across its strings

**do something over and over until it's done very well

Albert's Uncle Jakob was an engineer.*
What's wrong, Albert?
Oh, Uncle, I'm studying algebra.** I don't like it.
But algebra is fun!
It *is*?
Think of it this way: we are hunting for a little animal. We don't know its name, so we call it *X*.
We hunt for it and finally we *catch* it! Then we give it a name.
And now you have the answer! Do you understand?
Yes!

*someone who designs and builds machines, bridges, and other things

**a kind of arithmetic in which letters stand for numbers

Later, a young friend gave Albert some books.
I have brought you two books you may like, one on physics* and one on geometry.**
Thank you very much!
A few weeks later . . .
Oh, Max! There's a problem here you must help me with.
I'm sorry, Albert. You already know more than I do about physics and geometry.
But at school Albert had trouble.
Please, sir, may I ask a question?
You are not here to ask questions! You are to learn what is in your books, and to repeat it when you are asked to do so.
School is like the army. Everyone must do just what he is told.

*the study of such things as energy, heat, and electricity

**a branch of mathematics that deals with points, lines, and angles

Albert worried about the army.
Couldn't we move to another country? If I stay here I'll have to be a soldier.
Why, son, you are too young for the army!
There is no need to worry about that now!
Meanwhile, Albert's father was having trouble with his business.
Things are not good in Germany, but I can get a job in Italy.
Then we will move to Italy!
That's just what I want!
Oh, no, son. You must stay here and finish school.
Someday you will go to college.

So Albert was left behind to stay with relatives.*
He was very unhappy.
Then one day the principal sent for him.
You must leave school! You ask too many questions, and you set a bad example for your classmates.
You mean I really have to go? Hurray!
Albert joined his parents in Italy.
He loved it.
He went to art galleries.**
He also learned to sail.
He listened to music.
He even climbed mountains.

*aunts, uncles, cousins
**places where paintings are shown to the public

But a few months later, his father came to him with a plan.
Perhaps you should become an engineer.
But he can't go to college. He has no diploma.*
In Switzerland there is a school you can attend, but you must pass a test. It is worth trying.
So sixteen-year-old Albert went to Zurich, Switzerland and took the test.
He failed. But the school principal spoke to him.
You are very good in mathematics!** If you go to the high school in Aarau for a year, you will be able to pass our test.
Aarau was twenty miles from Zurich. Albert lived with a teacher's family. He loved the school and the people of Switzerland.
The school is wonderful! The teachers answer our questions! They help us think for ourselves.

*a document proving that a person has finished high school

**the study of numbers; arithmetic

After a year, Albert was able to enter college. He worked hard but didn't have much money.

Yet there was much to enjoy.
I have seen that girl in mathematics class.
Her name is Mileva Maritsch.

Soon Albert knew Mileva very well.
When I finish school and find a job, we can be married.

Another good friend and classmate was Marcel Grossman.
There are new ideas that may change everything we know about the world. But they are not yet taught here!

I can't study the new ideas and still keep up with my classes.
Go on with your studying. I will take notes in class and share them with you.
Thanks to Marcel, Albert passed his tests.

In August, 1900, he and his friends finished college.
What will you do now, Albert?
I want to be a teacher!
But Albert had not wanted to go to his classes when he was a student. So now the school did not want to hire him as a teacher.
I need a job. But first I will become a citizen of Switzerland.
The people here are kind and free. I feel more at home here than I ever did in Germany.
In 1901, Albert finally became a citizen of Switzerland. It made him very proud and happy.
In 1902, Marcel helped him get a job in the Swiss patent office.*
Your job is to study the model and then write up papers that will protect the inventor.**
I understand.

*an office that gives papers to inventors so that no one else can make or sell their inventions

**a person who plans and builds something for the first time

Albert made many friends.
I can live on what I make. And my job gives me time to work on my own ideas.
So he sent for Mileva, and they were married.
We hope you will be happy!
The next year, the Einsteins had a son, Hans Albert.
Albert?
Hello! Come in!
Whatever else Albert might be doing, he always had a book nearby.
There was always a notebook* in his pocket.
H'mm . . . yes!

*a small book with blank pages used for taking notes

In 1905, four papers he had written were printed in a magazine. One of them would help to bring him a Nobel Prize* sixteen years later.
He wrote to a friend.
The first paper is about light, and the fourth changes our ideas of space and time.

*Most people never heard of these papers. But scientists** all over the world were excited about them.*

In Poland . . .
Einstein is very smart!
In Germany . . .
We must study this paper!
But some people felt differently.
Einstein is crazy!
The teachers at Albert's college were sorry they hadn't hired him.
Einstein is one of your teachers, isn't he?
Well, no. But perhaps he will soon teach here!
Before, no one would hire him to teach. Now Albert had a choice of jobs.

*a famous prize given each year to people whose work is very important

**people who study the laws of nature

In 1909, he began teaching at the University of Zurich. In 1911, he was offered a job at the University of Prague in Czechoslovakia.
In Prague I would have a better job—with more time for my own work.
Then we should go to Prague.
They want to know what my religion* is.
I am a Jew.** But I don't think a person's religion should make any difference in the way he is treated.
In Prague life was better for the Einsteins.
When we were students, we had oil lamps. Now we have electric light!
And a maid!

*a set of beliefs about God

**a person who follows the teachings of the Old Testament in the Bible

But there were some things that troubled Albert.
The Germans here look down on the Czechs.* The Czechs hate the Germans. And the Jews are set apart from everyone else.

Nevertheless, Albert's work went well. He was becoming well known among scientists in Europe. Many colleges invited him to come and speak. Several even offered him jobs.
After eighteen months in Prague, the Einsteins returned to Zurich.
This is the school where I could not get a teaching job! Now they want me here at last.

The students liked his lectures.**
If you don't understand, please ask questions!

Albert was always thinking about a new idea.
One moment—I must write this idea down.

*people from Czechoslovakia

**talks given to teach people about a subject

One day he had visitors from Germany.
We want you to come and work in Germany.
You will be in charge of a new school of physics. You will make a great deal of money.
You may teach or you may spend all your time studying.
It is a fine offer. But I will come only if I can remain a citizen* of Switzerland.
The Germans agreed. So the Einsteins moved to Berlin in April, 1914. But soon they agreed to separate, and Mileva went back to Zurich with their sons.
It is best for us to divorce,** but we will still be friends.
And if ever I win the Nobel Prize, I will give the money to you!
Albert found Berlin full of German soldiers.
This is such a big army. There is sure to be a war.

*a person who belongs to a certain country by birth or by choice
**legally end a marriage

Albert was right. In August, the Germans invaded Belgium. Soon the world was at war.
We have written a paper saying that Germany is not to blame for the war. It is signed by ninety-three well-known scientists, writers, and artists. Will you sign it?
No!
Instead, Albert joined with a pacifist,* George Nicolai. They wrote their own paper.
We will look for help from Germans who want to work for peace.
Yes, we must stop the war.
They could find only two other Germans to sign their paper. But Einstein wrote letters, went to meetings, and made speeches. Everywhere he spoke against the war.
He also worked very hard at his job. Finally, in 1915, he finished another paper.
It is done!
Albert had relatives in Berlin. One was a young widow** with two daughters.
I remember you when we were children. Do you still play the violin?
Yes, Elsa!

*someone who doesn't believe in war and who works against it

**a woman whose husband has died

In 1918, Germany surrendered* and the war ended. In 1919, Albert and Elsa were married.
My paper says that light traveling from the stars to the earth will be bent as it passes the sun.
This idea could be proved during an eclipse of the sun.**
Other scientists wanted to test Einstein's idea, too. In England . . .
If we have people in Brazil and at Principe Island off South Africa, we should get fine views of the eclipse.
We'll do it!
So on May 29, scientists took pictures of the eclipse.
Quick! Another picture! The eclipse will last only two minutes!

*gave up

**the covering of the sun by the moon as it passes between the earth and the sun

Soon we will see the pictures.
Finally, he had the answer.
My pictures prove that Einstein is right!
Soon Albert was famous.* Everywhere in the world people wanted to know more about him.
What is it, Elsa?
Reporters!** Dozens of them!
Sir, please explain your theory of relativity.
How do you bend light?
How did you get started in this work?
Has everyone gone crazy?

*well known

**people who write stories for newspapers

He received mail from all over the world.
How will I read it all?
There's more outside!
MAIL
People stopped him on the street.
Please sign my book!
Don't move! I want to take your picture!
Scientists honored him, and he was offered jobs in many countries. But in Germany there were still problems.
Some Germans now hate me because I am a Jew and a pacifist. Perhaps I should leave Germany.
No, we need you here.
Maybe there *is* hope for peace in Europe. I will stay and help.

Not long afterward, Albert met with the leader of a Zionist group.*
I never believed that people should be separated by their religion. But now I see that Jews need a place to call home.
Then come with me to the United States to raise money.

Albert agreed, and the Einsteins arrived in New York in April, 1921. Reporters crowded the ship.
Mrs. Einstein, do *you* understand the theory of relativity?
Oh, no. But I am happy anyway!

Everywhere he went, great crowds welcomed him.
Millions of dollars were raised to help the Jews.

*a movement to build a Jewish state in Palestine, the ancient home of the Jews

He was invited to the White House. Columbia University gave him a medal. At Princeton University, he received an honorary degree.*
In the next few years, he visited many countries. All over the world he was honored and loved.
Albert, you have won the Nobel Prize!
That's very nice. I promised to give the money to Mileva to pay for my sons' schooling.
In Japan, a holiday was held in honor of Albert.
But in Germany, the government blamed the Jews for many of Germany's problems. And because Einstein was a Jew, life was hard, even dangerous, for him.
Albert, please leave Germany! The Nazis** will kill you!
The Nazi party is only a small part of Germany. I must stay here and help to defeat them.

*a diploma given as an honor to a great person
**Germans who followed Adolf Hitler, the man who led Germany from 1933 to 1945

But during the next ten years, the Nazi party in Germany grew stronger. And Einstein had a visitor from America.
We would like you to work in Princeton, New Jersey. You would head a group of scholars* there.
Perhaps I could spend a few months each year in Princeton.
Meanwhile, his family and friends grew more afraid for his safety.
The Nazis grow stronger every day.
They call your theory of relativity a plot** by Jews against the world.
We hear they have offered a $5,000 reward to anyone who will kill you.
I never thought I was worth so much.
Albert, this is no joke! *Please*—you must leave Germany.
The trip is planned. I will go the United States to spend the winter teaching in California.

*people who have studied a great deal in one field

**a secret plan for doing something evil

After the winter in California, the Einsteins prepared to leave for Germany.
Sir, Hitler has been chosen by the people as Germany's leader!
Then I will not go back.
So, after a short trip to Europe, the Einsteins returned to the United States and settled in Princeton.
President Roosevelt invited them to the White House.
I understand you like to sail.
Yes, I do.
In 1940, Einstein became a citizen of the United States.
Meanwhile, other great scientists also left Europe because it was dangerous for them there.
We know that the Germans will soon be able to make atomic bombs.*
That's terrible!

*huge bombs that can destroy a whole city in one blast

I will write to President Roosevelt about this.

Einstein's letter to Roosevelt became famous. Because of it, the United States began to work on the bomb, too. Meanwhile, German armies attacked Europe, and Japanese planes bombed the United States at Pearl Harbor.

But on August 6, 1945, the United States exploded an atomic bomb over Hiroshima, Japan. The war was over.
Einstein was sorry the bomb had ever been made. In 1946, he joined with other scientists to warn the world of the results* of the bomb.
We must protect the world from such bombs. This means that we must prevent** another world war.

*things that happen because of something else
**keep from happening

Until his death in April, 1955, Einstein lived a quiet life in Princeton.
We have four tiny new kittens at my house!
How wonderful! Will you take me to see them?

But he never stopped working.
The important thing is to keep asking questions. Every day we can understand a little more about the world.

And he kept up his fight for peace.
Our choice is simple: either we give up war, or the world will be destroyed.

end

Do you remember?

When Einstein was five years old, his father brought him a gift that he loved. It was a:

a. bird. b. music box. c. compass.

Einstein graduated from the Swiss Federal Polytechnic Institute and:

a. became a teacher.
b. became an electrical engineer.
c. worked in the Swiss Patent Office.

After talking with other scientists, Einstein wrote to President Roosevelt about the:

a. space program.
b. atomic bomb.
c. high cost of food.

Because atomic bombs destroy so many lives and homes, Einstein joined with other scientists to:

a. form a new research institute.
b. warn the world that wars must be prevented.
c. go sailing to find peace.

Words to know

Can you use these words in sentences of your own?

patent office
eclipse of the sun
pacifist
honorary degree
atomic bombs
scholars
physics
engineer
geometry

True or false

1. Because Einstein was so interested in mathematics and physics, he never bothered with things like music and art.

2. As a boy, Einstein was dismissed from school because he was always fighting.

3. Einstein hated war and worked against it all he could.

4. In 1940, Einstein became a United States citizen.

5. In Einstein's time, students were not allowed to ask questions in the classroom.

Questions to think about and discuss

1. Name the many different things Einstein did that backed up his beliefs about war.

2. What were the schools like during Einstein's time? What especially bothered him about the way schools were run?

3. How did Einstein feel about Germany *before* World War I? How did he feel about it *after* World War I? What countries did he like better? Why?

4. How do you think Einstein would feel today about all our bombs and missiles? How would he feel about our space programs? Give reasons for your answers.

5. What is the Zionist movement? What did Einstein do to promote it? Why is it that a well-known person can do so much more for a good cause than someone who is not?